# Things we do

### First-time stories to share and enjoy

This edition first published in Great Britain 2001
by Egmont Children's Books Limited
a division of Egmont Holding Limited
239 Kensington High Street, London W8 6SA
Text and design copyright © 2001 Egmont Children's Books Limited

*My New Haircut*
First published in Great Britain 2000
by Egmont Children's Books Limited
Illustrated by Jan Lewis.
Text by Laura Dollin. Designed by Daniel Devlin.
Copyright © 2000 Egmont Children's Books Limited

*My Visit to the Doctor*
First published in Great Britain 2000
by Egmont Children's Books Limited
Illustrated by Priscilla Lamont.
Text by Susan Hitches. With acknowledgements to Dr Melinda Creme.
Designed by Mandy Norman.
Copyright © 2000 Egmont Children's Books Limited

*We're Going Swimming*
First published in Great Britain 2000
by Egmont Children's Books Limited
Illustrated by Ann Kronheimer.
Text by Siobhán Sheerin. Designed by Suzanne Cocks.
Copyright © 2000 Egmont Children's Books Limited

*Going to Nursery*
First published in Great Britain 2000
by Egmont Children's Books Limited
Illustrated by Amelia Rosato.
Text by Laura Dollin. Designed by Mandy Norman.
With special thanks to the Brodetsky Nursery School for their help during research.
Copyright © 2000 Egmont Children's Books Limited

*Ben Goes Out to Eat*
First published in Great Britain 2000
by Egmont Children's Books Limited
Illustrated by Ann Johns.
Text by Katy Rodda. Designed by Karina Edginton-Vigus.
Copyright © 2000 Egmont Children's Books Limited

ISBN 0 7497 4640 8

Printed in Hong Kong

1 3 5 7 9 10 8 6 4 2

# Contents

# My New Haircut

We're going to the hairdresser.
We mustn't be late.

quick

quick

Charlie and Joe are having their hair cut.
"You can come and watch, Maggie,"
Mum says to me.

Brmmm
brmmm
brmmm
bumpity
bump
bump

All kinds of funny people are sitting on the bus. Long hair, short hair, pink hair, no hair!

"Can I have my hair like that?"
Joe thinks Charlie is very silly!

The hairdresser has almost
no hair at all!

**Busy, busy, busy,** lots for us to see.

Charlie goes first.
Mum can read the paper.

glug glug glug

"Look at all the fish!"

There is lots of squirty water.
"Shut your eyes tight!"
the hairdresser says.

Now it's Joe's turn to wear
a special overall.
I'd like to have **my** hair cut too!

**SNIP**

**SNIP**

**SNIP**

The scissors
cut their hair.

Charlie sits
still, but Joe
**wriggles**
around.

"Now, now, Joe, you must sit still."
Mum tells Joe that the scissors are sharp.

Whizz-whizz-whizz!

It's time for the hairdryer.

Oooh, I can feel the air, all blowy and warm!

Brushing
and combing

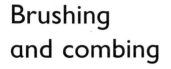

and then some
smelly gel.

"It's not fair! I want my hair cut too!"

"Alright, Maggie,"
says Mum to me.
"You've been so good
and the hairdresser
has time."

Yes Yes Yes

I'm very excited.
Now I can have my hair cut too!

"Ha-ha-ha!" say Charlie and Joe.
They think my hair is going to look like that.

**Spray** spray **spray** some water on my hair.

**SNIP SNIP SNIP**
the scissors go.

"Look at my hair falling onto the floor!"

**Whizz whizz whizz**

the hairdryer goes, and all my hair blows everywhere!

Last of all some smelly gel, just this once for a special treat.

"My, my, my, you **have** been good!"

The hairdresser gives a biscuit each
to Charlie, Joe and even to me!

"Aren't you lucky!"
says Mum to us.
"Now, what do you say?"

We all say thank you.
I hope we can come again one day.

**Bumpity-bump-bump,** all the way home.
Going to the hairdresser is lots of fun!

The End

# My Visit to the Doctor

"Grandma's taking you to see the doctor today," says Mum. "Tell me about it, Jack, when I come home from work."

"We're going to the Doctor after lunch,"
says Grandma. "She is going to have
a look in your ears, because they've been
hurting you."

"We're ready to go now," says Grandma. "You need your hat to keep your ears warm."

It's too hot!

It won't take long to get there," says Grandma.

"Jack has an appointment to see
the Doctor," says Grandma.
"Take a seat, please,"
says the lady at the desk.

"We'll have to wait for our turn," says
Grandma. "It shouldn't be too long, now."

"Come in, please," calls the Doctor.
"Jack hasn't been feeling well," says Grandma.
"His ears are very sore."

"Let's have a look at you then, Jack,"
says the Doctor kindly.
"Can I listen to your chest?"

"Now, I'll look at your throat,"
says the Doctor.
"Open your mouth wide."

"Which ear shall I look at first?"
asks the Doctor.

It tickles.

"Well done, Jack," says the Doctor.
"I think we'll give you something to make
your ears better."

"I'd like to see you again next week, please," says the Doctor.
"Thank you, Doctor," says Grandma.
"Goodbye."

"We're getting the medicine for you here," says Grandma.

"Time to go home, Jack," says Grandma. "But let's pop into the bakery first. It's over there, just next to the bookshop."

"You can choose a cake," says Grandma.

"You were a very good boy and Mum will be pleased."

"Hello, Jack," says Mum. "You'll soon feel well again. Let's have some tea, now."

"Save some cake for me," says Mum.
"You're looking better already."

The End

# We're Going Swimming

I'm so excited, my tummy feels funny. I got my first swimming badge last week, so I'm going swimming in the big pool today.

"What's that man going to do?" I ask.
"Judo, I think," says Dad. "There are lots
of different sports to do here."

In the changing room, Mum helps me undo my buttons but I can do everything else myself. I check to make sure my swimming badge won't come off.

I put money in the slot and close the locker door. The key is on a pink rubber band and Mum lets me put it on my wrist because I am going to the big pool.

Daniel can swim a little bit, but best of all he likes to splash around in the baby pool.

Dad climbs down into the water,
but I'm not sure I want to get in just yet.
"I can't see the bottom of the pool," I tell Dad.

"Will my feet touch the floor like yours, Dad?" I ask.
"Of course they will," he tells me.

The water makes his legs look funny and I can't stop laughing. I wiggle my toes in the water and it feels nice.

Lots of other people are in the water having fun, and some of them are even on the slide. I want to get in too, now.

The water's higher than in the little pool,
but I'm not very scared any more. When Dad
holds my hands I take my feet off the floor.

"This is fun, Dad. I like the big pool!" I shout.
"It's just the same as the little pool," Dad say
"but you're too grown up for that now,
aren't you?"

I'm swimming on my own now. The big pool is much more fun. Mum and Daniel have come to watch.
"Well done, Georgia," says Mum. "Do you want to go on the slide? I'll catch you."

I love the big pool!

The slide is the best thing today.
I'm going to make a big splash!

Daniel wriggles around when Dad tries to dry him with a big fluffy towel.

I'm almost dry now, my socks are still sticking to my feet! Mum squeezes our costumes and they drip all over the floor.

We go to the café upstairs. Mum brings sandwiches from home because we are always starving after swimming.

Daniel watches people through the glass window and Mum gives me money for the drinks machine. Mmmmm, orange juice. I can't wait!

"I want to go in the big pool, too," says Daniel.
"You will when you are big like me," I tell him.

The End

# Going to Nursery

Why must I go to nursery?
"You'll have lots of fun there, Nita," says Mum.

But Sammy doesn't have to go to nursery.
I don't want to go there at all today.

Why must I come
to nursery?
"Look at all the
fun things to do!"
says Mum.

But Mum doesn't stay for long at nursery.
I don't want to be by myself today.

Why must I be at nursery?
"Let's go and see what Tom's doing,"
the lady says to me.

But these toys are different from my toys at home. I don't see why I have to be here today.

Why must I come to nursery again? I've been here before and it's the same every day. I hang up my coat on my own special hook,

I **play** in the sandpit,

pretend I can **cook,**

... Build houses with Tom, get paper and glue ..

... for sticking
and colouring –
**so much to do!**

Red paint, blue paint, yellow paint, green,
I'm **painting** a picture
for Sammy and me!

Then it's time for a snack,
a drink and a story …

Maybe I like it at nursery today!

Another day at nursery, what shall I do?
"I'm playing the tambourine," Tom says to me

**Bang!**
**Bang!** **Bang!** **Bang!** My favourite is the drum!
I like it even better at nursery today.

# What shall we play in the garden outside?

I climb,

Tom climbs,

we both slide down!

Pedalling **fast** on red and yellow tricycles,
I'm having **lots** of fun at nursery today!

Why do I have to go home again now?
"It's time for some tea!" says Mum to me.

Today I'll take my painting home
to show to Dad and Sammy.
I can't wait to come back to nursery again!

The End

# Ben Goes
# Out to Eat

We're not eating at
home today.
We're going out instead.
"Wait for the lady,
boys," says Dad.

A waiter shows us where to sit.
"Hello. My name's Mike," he says.

"What would you like to drink?" asks Mike.
"Apple juice, please!" say Ryan and Matt.
"Three apple juices and a pot of tea, please,"
says Dad.

There's a special menu for me. "You'll be able to choose for yourself," says Mike.

"I want nuggets," says Matt.
"You have to say 'please'," Ryan says.
"As long as you have some vegetables, too,"
says Mum.

I don't know what to eat.
"Fish fingers?"

"A Burger?"

"Macaroni?"

"What about sausages?" says Mike.
"Ooh, yes please!"

Mike brings our drinks.
"What do you say to Mike?"
asks Mum.

Thank you

Thank you

"Look, we can make bubbles!" says Matt.
"Sshh, boys. Not everyone wants to hear you,"
says Mum.

I can hear lots of noises.

glug glug glug

"What's that?"
"That's coffee," says Dad.

crash-crash-tinkle

crunch munch

hatter chatter

"Everyone's eating except us," says Ryan.

rumble rumble

"We're hungry," says Matt.

Our food is here! "Here you are," says Mike.
"Can we start now?" asks Ryan.

Mum asks Matt if he likes his nuggets.
His mouth is too full of them to say anything!

"Try some pasta, Ben," says Dad.
Dad's food looks like slimy worms!
But I think it's very tasty.

"Look, Mum! A shoe!"
"What a lovely shoe," says Mum.
"Why don't you eat it up now?"

"Did you like your sausages?" Mike asks me
"They're my favourite food, too."

"Please can we get down now?" asks Ryan.
"Say 'thank you' to Mike first," says Dad.
"Who are these balloons for?"
asks Mum.

They're for us! "Thank you," I say.
I hope we can eat here again soon.